With These

Thoughts

Set In Soul

This Journal Belongs To

_____

Dedicated To The Heart And Spirit With A Message That Needs To Be Heard.

Table Of Contents

How To Use This Journal

If you are interested in getting back into writing, explore your love for writing or even just start to develop your skills in writing, then this journal is for you. This journal can be used to write poems, scripts, stories, articles, songs and more. This journal is your space where you can express your thoughts and track your growth in your writing skills. This journal also serves as your place of accountability. We recommend that you write everyday even when you don't feel like writing. This is because when you write even when you don't want to, you are pushing out within you something that is being tucked away. Some days you will experience writer's block and that is okay. That is when you still write down thoughts and ideas of how to overcome your writer's block. We recommend you write at night or when inspired to during the day (but for the most part at night). You have something important to tell the world and many special eyes are ready to see what you put on display.

About My Writing

About My Writing

When Did I Start Writing (Answer If Applicable)?

I Started Writing Because (Answer If Applicable):

I Want To Start Writing Because (Answer If Applicable):

I Like To Write About:

I Want To Write:

About My Writing

My Style Of Writing:

When I Write, I Feel:

I Am Trying To Write:

When I'm Done Writing, I Feel:

I Mainly Write About:

About My Writing

I Write About What I Answered In The Previous Prompt Because:

When I Write About What I Answered In The Previous Two Prompts, It Makes Me Feel:

In The Past, I Have Written:

I Believe I Have Gotten My Writing Skills From:

I Choose To Express Myself With Writing Because:

About My Writing

I Want To Step Into Writing:

I Get My Ideas From:

I Am Inspired By:

I've Been Writing Since (Answer If Applicable):

I Believe That When I Write:

About My Writing

I Write For:

My Writing Has Changed Over The Years (Answer If Applicable):

I Use To Write About (Answer If Applicable):

Now I Write About:

I Look Forward To Writing:

About My Writing

Writing Is A Form Of:

I Have Felt That My Writings:

I Am Struggling To Write About:

People In My Family That Are/Were Writers:

Who Do I Want To Read My Writings?

About My Writing

I Would Like My Writings To Transform:

I Would Like To Start Writing:

I've Taken Breaks From Writing To:

When I Have Writer's Block, I:

I Am Known To Write About:

About My Writing

I Have Always Written As A Way To:

When I Am In Pain, I Write:

When I Am In Love, I Write:

When I Am Grateful, I Write:

I Consider My Work:

About My Writing

The Types Of Books I Like To Read (Answer If Applicable):

The Goal With My Writing Is To:

I Would Like My Writings To Reach:

When Someone Reads My Writings, I Want Them To:

I'm Learning To Write:

About My Writing

My Favorite Writer Is:

Some Great Authors Are:

Some Great Songwriters Are:

Some Great Scriptwriters Are:

I Like To Write Before I:

About My Writing

I Like To Write After I:

I Have Difficulty:

I Can Easily:

My Favorite Poem Is:

I Want My Writings To Help Others:

About My Writing

My Focus Is On:

I Write So I Can:

If Someone Was To Write A Story About Me, It Would Be:

I Would Say My Mind Is:

I Believe I Can:

About My Writing

I Know Within Me Is:

I Believe My Writings Are:

I Stopped Putting Pressure On Myself To:

I Started Putting Pressure On Myself To:

I Feel Like I Must Complete:

About My Writing

To Me, A Great Writer Is:

To Me, A Great Writer Does:

I Want My Work To:

I Want To Write A Novel About (Answer If Applicable):

I Want To Write A Screenplay About (Answer If Applicable):

About My Writing

I Want To Write A Poem About (Answer If Applicable):

I Want To Write A Song About (Answer If Applicable):

The Different Types Of Writing Scripts I Can Write In:

My Beautiful Story

My Beautiful Story

Date:

I Feel:

Today I Was Inspired By:

The Conveying Message:

Today's Writing Topic:

The What Ifs/How In What Your Writing (Answer If Applicable):

Today's Emotions:

Today I Dealt With Writer's Block By (Answer If Applicable):

The Characters (If Applicable):

Today's Writing

My Beautiful Story

Date:

I Feel:

Today I Was Inspired By:

The Conveying Message:

Today's Writing Topic:

The What Ifs/How In What Your Writing (Answer If Applicable):

Today's Emotions:

Today I Dealt With Writer's Block By (Answer If Applicable):

The Characters (If Applicable):

Today's Writing

I HAVE TO GET EVERYTHING OUT.

I AM A WRITER.

My Beautiful Story

Date:

I Feel:

Today I Was Inspired By:

The Conveying Message:

Today's Writing Topic:

The What Ifs/How In What Your Writing (Answer If Applicable):

Today's Emotions:

Today I Dealt With Writer's Block By (Answer If Applicable):

The Characters (If Applicable):

Today's Writing

My Beautiful Story

Date:

I Feel:

Today I Was Inspired By:

The Conveying Message:

Today's Writing Topic:

The What Ifs/How In What Your Writing
(Answer If Applicable):

Today's Emotions:

Today I Dealt With Writer's Block By
(Answer If Applicable):

The Characters (If Applicable):

Today's Writing

My Beautiful Story

Date:

I Feel:

Today I Was Inspired By:

The Conveying Message:

Today's Writing Topic:

The What Ifs/How In What Your Writing (Answer If Applicable):

Today's Emotions:

Today I Dealt With Writer's Block By (Answer If Applicable):

The Characters (If Applicable):

Today's Writing

THERE IS SOMEONE WHO NEEDS TO HEAR MY STORY.

I Love Reading....

My Beautiful Story

Date: I Feel:

Today I Was Inspired By: The Conveying Message:

Today's Writing Topic: The What Ifs/How In What Your Writing
                                         (Answer If Applicable):

Today's Emotions: Today I Dealt With Writer's Block By
                                         (Answer If Applicable):

The Characters (If Applicable):

Today's Writing

My Beautiful Story

Date:

I Feel:

Today I Was Inspired By:

The Conveying Message:

Today's Writing Topic:

The What Ifs/How In What Your Writing (Answer If Applicable):

Today's Emotions:

Today I Dealt With Writer's Block By (Answer If Applicable):

The Characters (If Applicable):

Today's Writing

My Beautiful Story

Date: I Feel:

Today I Was Inspired By: The Conveying Message:

Today's Writing Topic: The What Ifs/How In What Your Writing
                                         (Answer If Applicable):

Today's Emotions: Today I Dealt With Writer's Block By
                                         (Answer If Applicable):

The Characters (If Applicable):

Today's Writing

I Am Currently Reading....

THERE IS SOMETHING UNIQUE IN THE WAY I TELL MY STORY.

My Beautiful Story

Date:

I Feel:

Today I Was Inspired By:

The Conveying Message:

Today's Writing Topic:

The What Ifs/How In What Your Writing (Answer If Applicable):

Today's Emotions:

Today I Dealt With Writer's Block By (Answer If Applicable):

The Characters (If Applicable):

Today's Writing

My Beautiful Story

Date:

I Feel:

Today I Was Inspired By:

The Conveying Message:

Today's Writing Topic:

The What Ifs/How In What Your Writing (Answer If Applicable):

Today's Emotions:

Today I Dealt With Writer's Block By (Answer If Applicable):

The Characters (If Applicable):

Today's Writing

My Beautiful Story

Date:

I Feel:

Today I Was Inspired By:

The Conveying Message:

Today's Writing Topic:

The What Ifs/How In What Your Writing (Answer If Applicable):

Today's Emotions:

Today I Dealt With Writer's Block By (Answer If Applicable):

The Characters (If Applicable):

Today's Writing

THIS IS ONE
STORY I
CAN WRITE
A GREAT
ENDING FOR.

I AM NOT JUST TELLING MY STORY,
I AM INSPIRING SOMEONE TO TELL THEIR OWN.

My Beautiful Story

Date:

I Feel:

Today I Was Inspired By:

The Conveying Message:

Today's Writing Topic:

The What Ifs/How In What Your Writing
(Answer If Applicable):

Today's Emotions:

Today I Dealt With Writer's Block By
(Answer If Applicable):

The Characters (If Applicable):

Today's Writing

My Beautiful Story

Date:

I Feel:

Today I Was Inspired By:

The Conveying Message:

Today's Writing Topic:

The What Ifs/How In What Your Writing (Answer If Applicable):

Today's Emotions:

Today I Dealt With Writer's Block By (Answer If Applicable):

The Characters (If Applicable):

Today's Writing

My Beautiful Story

Date:

I Feel:

Today I Was Inspired By:

The Conveying Message:

Today's Writing Topic:

The What Ifs/How In What Your Writing (Answer If Applicable):

Today's Emotions:

Today I Dealt With Writer's Block By (Answer If Applicable):

The Characters (If Applicable):

Today's Writing

Writing Is Important To Me Because....

THE ONLY STORY I WANT TO READ IS YOURS.

My Beautiful Story

Date:

I Feel:

Today I Was Inspired By:

The Conveying Message:

Today's Writing Topic:

The What Ifs/How In What Your Writing
(Answer If Applicable):

Today's Emotions:

Today I Dealt With Writer's Block By
(Answer If Applicable):

The Characters (If Applicable):

Today's Writing

My Beautiful Story

Date:

I Feel:

Today I Was Inspired By:

The Conveying Message:

Today's Writing Topic:

The What Ifs/How In What Your Writing
(Answer If Applicable):

Today's Emotions:

Today I Dealt With Writer's Block By
(Answer If Applicable):

The Characters (If Applicable):

Today's Writing

THERE IS BEAUTY IN SAYING A LOT IN A FEW WORDS.

WHEN I READ YOUR WORDS, I FELT YOU.

My Beautiful Story

Date:

I Feel:

Today I Was Inspired By:

The Conveying Message:

Today's Writing Topic:

The What Ifs/How In What Your Writing (Answer If Applicable):

Today's Emotions:

Today I Dealt With Writer's Block By (Answer If Applicable):

The Characters (If Applicable):

Today's Writing

My Beautiful Story

Date:

I Feel:

Today I Was Inspired By:

The Conveying Message:

Today's Writing Topic:

The What Ifs/How In What Your Writing (Answer If Applicable):

Today's Emotions:

Today I Dealt With Writer's Block By (Answer If Applicable):

The Characters (If Applicable):

Today's Writing

My Beautiful Story

Date: I Feel:

Today I Was Inspired By: The Conveying Message:

Today's Writing Topic: The What Ifs/How In What Your Writing
                                         (Answer If Applicable):

Today's Emotions: Today I Dealt With Writer's Block By
                                         (Answer If Applicable):

The Characters (If Applicable):

Today's Writing

YOUR WORDS HELPED ME TO LET GO.

When I Write, I Am Releasing....

My Beautiful Story

Date:

I Feel:

Today I Was Inspired By:

The Conveying Message:

Today's Writing Topic:

The What Ifs/How In What Your Writing (Answer If Applicable):

Today's Emotions:

Today I Dealt With Writer's Block By (Answer If Applicable):

The Characters (If Applicable):

Today's Writing

My Beautiful Story

Date: I Feel:

Today I Was Inspired By: The Conveying Message:

Today's Writing Topic: The What Ifs/How In What Your Writing
                                               (Answer If Applicable):

Today's Emotions: Today I Dealt With Writer's Block By
                                               (Answer If Applicable):

The Characters (If Applicable):

Today's Writing

NOW > LATER
SO THAT IT
WON'T LEAD
TO NEVER.

WRITING MYSELF OUT OF WRITER'S BLOCK.

My Beautiful Story

Date:

I Feel:

Today I Was Inspired By:

The Conveying Message:

Today's Writing Topic:

The What Ifs/How In What Your Writing
(Answer If Applicable):

Today's Emotions:

Today I Dealt With Writer's Block By
(Answer If Applicable):

The Characters (If Applicable):

Today's Writing

My Beautiful Story

Date:

I Feel:

Today I Was Inspired By:

The Conveying Message:

Today's Writing Topic:

The What Ifs/How In What Your Writing (Answer If Applicable):

Today's Emotions:

Today I Dealt With Writer's Block By (Answer If Applicable):

The Characters (If Applicable):

Today's Writing

My Beautiful Story

Date:

I Feel:

Today I Was Inspired By:

The Conveying Message:

Today's Writing Topic:

The What Ifs/How In What Your Writing (Answer If Applicable):

Today's Emotions:

Today I Dealt With Writer's Block By (Answer If Applicable):

The Characters (If Applicable):

Today's Writing

SOME THINGS NEED TO BE SAID BY ME.

I LOVE WRITING OUT MY DREAMS.

I AM THE WRITER THAT I LOVE HEARING FROM.

I Consider Myself....

My Beautiful Story

Date:

I Feel:

Today I Was Inspired By:

The Conveying Message:

Today's Writing Topic:

The What Ifs/How In What Your Writing
(Answer If Applicable):

Today's Emotions:

Today I Dealt With Writer's Block By
(Answer If Applicable):

The Characters (If Applicable):

Today's Writing

My Beautiful Story

Date:

I Feel:

Today I Was Inspired By:

The Conveying Message:

Today's Writing Topic:

The What Ifs/How In What Your Writing (Answer If Applicable):

Today's Emotions:

Today I Dealt With Writer's Block By (Answer If Applicable):

The Characters (If Applicable):

Today's Writing

My Beautiful Story

Date:

I Feel:

Today I Was Inspired By:

The Conveying Message:

Today's Writing Topic:

The What Ifs/How In What Your Writing (Answer If Applicable):

Today's Emotions:

Today I Dealt With Writer's Block By (Answer If Applicable):

The Characters (If Applicable):

Today's Writing

I Started To Take Seriously....

SEEING MY EARLIER WRITINGS AND THINKING 'THAT WAS DEEP.'

My Beautiful Story

Date:

I Feel:

Today I Was Inspired By:

The Conveying Message:

Today's Writing Topic:

The What Ifs/How In What Your Writing (Answer If Applicable):

Today's Emotions:

Today I Dealt With Writer's Block By (Answer If Applicable):

The Characters (If Applicable):

Today's Writing

My Beautiful Story

Date:

I Feel:

Today I Was Inspired By:

The Conveying Message:

Today's Writing Topic:

The What Ifs/How In What Your Writing (Answer If Applicable):

Today's Emotions:

Today I Dealt With Writer's Block By (Answer If Applicable):

The Characters (If Applicable):

Today's Writing

My Beautiful Story

Date:

I Feel:

Today I Was Inspired By:

The Conveying Message:

Today's Writing Topic:

The What Ifs/How In What Your Writing (Answer If Applicable):

Today's Emotions:

Today I Dealt With Writer's Block By (Answer If Applicable):

The Characters (If Applicable):

Today's Writing

My Beautiful Story

Date:

I Feel:

Today I Was Inspired By:

The Conveying Message:

Today's Writing Topic:

The What Ifs/How In What Your Writing (Answer If Applicable):

Today's Emotions:

Today I Dealt With Writer's Block By (Answer If Applicable):

The Characters (If Applicable):

Today's Writing

SOMEONE IS WAITING ON THAT MESSAGE FROM ME.

I Want To Create....

My Beautiful Story

Date:

I Feel:

Today I Was Inspired By:

The Conveying Message:

Today's Writing Topic:

The What Ifs/How In What Your Writing (Answer If Applicable):

Today's Emotions:

Today I Dealt With Writer's Block By (Answer If Applicable):

The Characters (If Applicable):

Today's Writing

My Beautiful Story

Date:

I Feel:

Today I Was Inspired By:

The Conveying Message:

Today's Writing Topic:

The What Ifs/How In What Your Writing (Answer If Applicable):

Today's Emotions:

Today I Dealt With Writer's Block By (Answer If Applicable):

The Characters (If Applicable):

Today's Writing

I Believe....

GOOD MORNING. IT'S TIME TO WRITE.

My Beautiful Story

Date: I Feel:

Today I Was Inspired By: The Conveying Message:

Today's Writing Topic: The What Ifs/How In What Your Writing
                                                   (Answer If Applicable):

Today's Emotions: Today I Dealt With Writer's Block By
                                                   (Answer If Applicable):

The Characters (If Applicable):

Today's Writing

My Beautiful Story

Date:

I Feel:

Today I Was Inspired By:

The Conveying Message:

Today's Writing Topic:

The What Ifs/How In What Your Writing (Answer If Applicable):

Today's Emotions:

Today I Dealt With Writer's Block By (Answer If Applicable):

The Characters (If Applicable):

Today's Writing

My Beautiful Story

Date:

I Feel:

Today I Was Inspired By:

The Conveying Message:

Today's Writing Topic:

The What Ifs/How In What Your Writing
(Answer If Applicable):

Today's Emotions:

Today I Dealt With Writer's Block By
(Answer If Applicable):

The Characters (If Applicable):

Today's Writing

THE SOUL BECOMES AT EASE WHEN YOU WRITE WHAT YOU FEEL.

WRITE YOUR TRUTH.

My Beautiful Story

Date:

I Feel:

Today I Was Inspired By:

The Conveying Message:

Today's Writing Topic:

The What Ifs/How In What Your Writing (Answer If Applicable):

Today's Emotions:

Today I Dealt With Writer's Block By (Answer If Applicable):

The Characters (If Applicable):

Today's Writing

My Beautiful Story

Date: I Feel:

Today I Was Inspired By: The Conveying Message:

Today's Writing Topic: The What Ifs/How In What Your Writing
                                           (Answer If Applicable):

Today's Emotions: Today I Dealt With Writer's Block By
                                           (Answer If Applicable):

The Characters (If Applicable):

Today's Writing

WISE WORDS AREN'T ALWAYS PRETTY.

I Like To Challenge Myself By....

My Beautiful Story

Date:

I Feel:

Today I Was Inspired By:

The Conveying Message:

Today's Writing Topic:

The What Ifs/How In What Your Writing (Answer If Applicable):

Today's Emotions:

Today I Dealt With Writer's Block By (Answer If Applicable):

The Characters (If Applicable):

Today's Writing

My Beautiful Story

Date:

I Feel:

Today I Was Inspired By:

The Conveying Message:

Today's Writing Topic:

The What Ifs/How In What Your Writing (Answer If Applicable):

Today's Emotions:

Today I Dealt With Writer's Block By (Answer If Applicable):

The Characters (If Applicable):

Today's Writing

My Beautiful Story

Date: I Feel:

Today I Was Inspired By: The Conveying Message:

Today's Writing Topic: The What Ifs/How In What Your Writing
                                         (Answer If Applicable):

Today's Emotions: Today I Dealt With Writer's Block By
                                         (Answer If Applicable):

The Characters (If Applicable):

Today's Writing

Writing Connects Me To ....

MY WORDS WILL CHANGE THE WORLD.

My Beautiful Story

Date:

I Feel:

Today I Was Inspired By:

The Conveying Message:

Today's Writing Topic:

The What Ifs/How In What Your Writing
(Answer If Applicable):

Today's Emotions:

Today I Dealt With Writer's Block By
(Answer If Applicable):

The Characters (If Applicable):

Today's Writing

My Beautiful Story

Date:

I Feel:

Today I Was Inspired By:

The Conveying Message:

Today's Writing Topic:

The What Ifs/How In What Your Writing (Answer If Applicable):

Today's Emotions:

Today I Dealt With Writer's Block By (Answer If Applicable):

The Characters (If Applicable):

Today's Writing

My Beautiful Story

Date:

I Feel:

Today I Was Inspired By:

The Conveying Message:

Today's Writing Topic:

The What Ifs/How In What Your Writing (Answer If Applicable):

Today's Emotions:

Today I Dealt With Writer's Block By (Answer If Applicable):

The Characters (If Applicable):

Today's Writing

My Beautiful Story

Date:

I Feel:

Today I Was Inspired By:

The Conveying Message:

Today's Writing Topic:

The What Ifs/How In What Your Writing
(Answer If Applicable):

Today's Emotions:

Today I Dealt With Writer's Block By
(Answer If Applicable):

The Characters (If Applicable):

Today's Writing

My Beautiful Story

Date:

I Feel:

Today I Was Inspired By:

The Conveying Message:

Today's Writing Topic:

The What Ifs/How In What Your Writing (Answer If Applicable):

Today's Emotions:

Today I Dealt With Writer's Block By (Answer If Applicable):

The Characters (If Applicable):

Today's Writing

THE MOST CHALLENGING PART IS STARTING FROM THE BEGINNING.

IMAGINE IT THEN CREATE IT.

My Beautiful Story

Date:

I Feel:

Today I Was Inspired By:

The Conveying Message:

Today's Writing Topic:

The What Ifs/How In What Your Writing (Answer If Applicable):

Today's Emotions:

Today I Dealt With Writer's Block By (Answer If Applicable):

The Characters (If Applicable):

Today's Writing

My Beautiful Story

Date:

I Feel:

Today I Was Inspired By:

The Conveying Message:

Today's Writing Topic:

The What Ifs/How In What Your Writing (Answer If Applicable):

Today's Emotions:

Today I Dealt With Writer's Block By (Answer If Applicable):

The Characters (If Applicable):

Today's Writing

My Beautiful Story

Date:

I Feel:

Today I Was Inspired By:

The Conveying Message:

Today's Writing Topic:

The What Ifs/How In What Your Writing (Answer If Applicable):

Today's Emotions:

Today I Dealt With Writer's Block By (Answer If Applicable):

The Characters (If Applicable):

Today's Writing

My Beautiful Story

Date:

I Feel:

Today I Was Inspired By:

The Conveying Message:

Today's Writing Topic:

The What Ifs/How In What Your Writing (Answer If Applicable):

Today's Emotions:

Today I Dealt With Writer's Block By (Answer If Applicable):

The Characters (If Applicable):

Today's Writing

When I Look Back At What I Use To Write, I....

I AM AN ARTIST. I CREATE WITH MY WORDS.

My Beautiful Story

Date:

I Feel:

Today I Was Inspired By:

The Conveying Message:

Today's Writing Topic:

The What Ifs/How In What Your Writing
(Answer If Applicable):

Today's Emotions:

Today I Dealt With Writer's Block By
(Answer If Applicable):

The Characters (If Applicable):

Today's Writing

My Beautiful Story

Date:

I Feel:

Today I Was Inspired By:

The Conveying Message:

Today's Writing Topic:

The What Ifs/How In What Your Writing (Answer If Applicable):

Today's Emotions:

Today I Dealt With Writer's Block By (Answer If Applicable):

The Characters (If Applicable):

Today's Writing

My Beautiful Story

Date:

I Feel:

Today I Was Inspired By:

The Conveying Message:

Today's Writing Topic:

The What Ifs/How In What Your Writing (Answer If Applicable):

Today's Emotions:

Today I Dealt With Writer's Block By (Answer If Applicable):

The Characters (If Applicable):

Today's Writing

IN THIS SPACE THAT I AM IN, ANYTHING IS POSSIBLE.

Publishing Vs Self Publishing....

I Prefer....

My Beautiful Story

Date:

I Feel:

Today I Was Inspired By:

The Conveying Message:

Today's Writing Topic:

The What Ifs/How In What Your Writing
(Answer If Applicable):

Today's Emotions:

Today I Dealt With Writer's Block By
(Answer If Applicable):

The Characters (If Applicable):

Today's Writing

My Beautiful Story

Date:

I Feel:

Today I Was Inspired By:

The Conveying Message:

Today's Writing Topic:

The What Ifs/How In What Your Writing (Answer If Applicable):

Today's Emotions:

Today I Dealt With Writer's Block By (Answer If Applicable):

The Characters (If Applicable):

Today's Writing

My Beautiful Story

Date: I Feel:

Today I Was Inspired By: The Conveying Message:

Today's Writing Topic: The What Ifs/How In What Your Writing
                                         (Answer If Applicable):

Today's Emotions: Today I Dealt With Writer's Block By
                                         (Answer If Applicable):

The Characters (If Applicable):

Today's Writing

I Want People To Read My Work And Say....

EVERY WRITER HAS OVERCOME SOMETHING.

My Beautiful Story

Date:

I Feel:

Today I Was Inspired By:

The Conveying Message:

Today's Writing Topic:

The What Ifs/How In What Your Writing (Answer If Applicable):

Today's Emotions:

Today I Dealt With Writer's Block By (Answer If Applicable):

The Characters (If Applicable):

Today's Writing

My Beautiful Story

Date:

I Feel:

Today I Was Inspired By:

The Conveying Message:

Today's Writing Topic:

The What Ifs/How In What Your Writing (Answer If Applicable):

Today's Emotions:

Today I Dealt With Writer's Block By (Answer If Applicable):

The Characters (If Applicable):

Today's Writing

My Beautiful Story

Date:

I Feel:

Today I Was Inspired By:

The Conveying Message:

Today's Writing Topic:

The What Ifs/How In What Your Writing (Answer If Applicable):

Today's Emotions:

Today I Dealt With Writer's Block By (Answer If Applicable):

The Characters (If Applicable):

Today's Writing

I STOPPED SAYING I WILL AND STARTED SAYING RIGHT NOW.

I THINK FASTER THAN I WRITE BUT I EXPRESS MYSELF BETTER WITH MY WORDS.

When I Write, I Bring To Life....

MY WORDS WILL BE WHAT SOMEONE LOVES TO READ.

My Beautiful Story

Date:

I Feel:

Today I Was Inspired By:

The Conveying Message:

Today's Writing Topic:

The What Ifs/How In What Your Writing (Answer If Applicable):

Today's Emotions:

Today I Dealt With Writer's Block By (Answer If Applicable):

The Characters (If Applicable):

Today's Writing

My Beautiful Story

Date:

I Feel:

Today I Was Inspired By:

The Conveying Message:

Today's Writing Topic:

The What Ifs/How In What Your Writing (Answer If Applicable):

Today's Emotions:

Today I Dealt With Writer's Block By (Answer If Applicable):

The Characters (If Applicable):

Today's Writing

My Beautiful Story

Date:

I Feel:

Today I Was Inspired By:

The Conveying Message:

Today's Writing Topic:

The What Ifs/How In What Your Writing (Answer If Applicable):

Today's Emotions:

Today I Dealt With Writer's Block By (Answer If Applicable):

The Characters (If Applicable):

Today's Writing

I HAVE
A TRUTH
I KNOW
SOMEONE CAN
RELATE TO.

What Do I Need Around Me Before I Write?

My Beautiful Story

Date:

I Feel:

Today I Was Inspired By:

The Conveying Message:

Today's Writing Topic:

The What Ifs/How In What Your Writing
(Answer If Applicable):

Today's Emotions:

Today I Dealt With Writer's Block By
(Answer If Applicable):

The Characters (If Applicable):

Today's Writing

My Beautiful Story

Date:

I Feel:

Today I Was Inspired By:

The Conveying Message:

Today's Writing Topic:

The What Ifs/How In What Your Writing (Answer If Applicable):

Today's Emotions:

Today I Dealt With Writer's Block By (Answer If Applicable):

The Characters (If Applicable):

Today's Writing

I FIND MYSELF IN THE THINGS I WRITE.

I Feel Misunderstood About....

My Beautiful Story

Date: I Feel:

Today I Was Inspired By: The Conveying Message:

Today's Writing Topic: The What Ifs/How In What Your Writing
                                              (Answer If Applicable):

Today's Emotions: Today I Dealt With Writer's Block By
                                              (Answer If Applicable):

The Characters (If Applicable):

Today's Writing

My Beautiful Story

Date: I Feel:

Today I Was Inspired By: The Conveying Message:

Today's Writing Topic: The What Ifs/How In What Your Writing
                                               (Answer If Applicable):

Today's Emotions: Today I Dealt With Writer's Block By
                                               (Answer If Applicable):

The Characters (If Applicable):

Today's Writing

My Beautiful Story

Date:

I Feel:

Today I Was Inspired By:

The Conveying Message:

Today's Writing Topic:

The What Ifs/How In What Your Writing (Answer If Applicable):

Today's Emotions:

Today I Dealt With Writer's Block By (Answer If Applicable):

The Characters (If Applicable):

Today's Writing

I Want To Recreate....

WHEN I WRITE, I CREATE SOMETHING BETTER.

My Beautiful Story

Date:

I Feel:

Today I Was Inspired By:

The Conveying Message:

Today's Writing Topic:

The What Ifs/How In What Your Writing (Answer If Applicable):

Today's Emotions:

Today I Dealt With Writer's Block By (Answer If Applicable):

The Characters (If Applicable):

Today's Writing

My Beautiful Story

Date:

I Feel:

Today I Was Inspired By:

The Conveying Message:

Today's Writing Topic:

The What Ifs/How In What Your Writing (Answer If Applicable):

Today's Emotions:

Today I Dealt With Writer's Block By (Answer If Applicable):

The Characters (If Applicable):

Today's Writing

My Beautiful Story

Date:

I Feel:

Today I Was Inspired By:

The Conveying Message:

Today's Writing Topic:

The What Ifs/How In What Your Writing (Answer If Applicable):

Today's Emotions:

Today I Dealt With Writer's Block By (Answer If Applicable):

The Characters (If Applicable):

Today's Writing

I TELL YOU THE THINGS I'VE ALWAYS WANTED TO SAY IN MY WRITING.

THIS ISN'T A LATE START. THIS IS THE PERFECT TIME.

My Beautiful Story

Date:

I Feel:

Today I Was Inspired By:

The Conveying Message:

Today's Writing Topic:

The What Ifs/How In What Your Writing (Answer If Applicable):

Today's Emotions:

Today I Dealt With Writer's Block By (Answer If Applicable):

The Characters (If Applicable):

Today's Writing

My Beautiful Story

Date: I Feel:

Today I Was Inspired By: The Conveying Message:

Today's Writing Topic: The What Ifs/How In What Your Writing
                                         (Answer If Applicable):

Today's Emotions: Today I Dealt With Writer's Block By
                                         (Answer If Applicable):

The Characters (If Applicable):

Today's Writing

My Beautiful Story

Date:

I Feel:

Today I Was Inspired By:

The Conveying Message:

Today's Writing Topic:

The What Ifs/How In What Your Writing (Answer If Applicable):

Today's Emotions:

Today I Dealt With Writer's Block By (Answer If Applicable):

The Characters (If Applicable):

Today's Writing

My Beautiful Story

Date:

I Feel:

Today I Was Inspired By:

The Conveying Message:

Today's Writing Topic:

The What Ifs/How In What Your Writing (Answer If Applicable):

Today's Emotions:

Today I Dealt With Writer's Block By (Answer If Applicable):

The Characters (If Applicable):

Today's Writing

IT'S BEAUTIFUL WHEN YOU CAN FEEL JUST A TENTH OF WHAT I FELT AND STILL APPRECIATE MY WORDS.

My Writing Gives....

My Beautiful Story

Date:

I Feel:

Today I Was Inspired By:

The Conveying Message:

Today's Writing Topic:

The What Ifs/How In What Your Writing
(Answer If Applicable):

Today's Emotions:

Today I Dealt With Writer's Block By
(Answer If Applicable):

The Characters (If Applicable):

Today's Writing

My Beautiful Story

Date:

I Feel:

Today I Was Inspired By:

The Conveying Message:

Today's Writing Topic:

The What Ifs/How In What Your Writing (Answer If Applicable):

Today's Emotions:

Today I Dealt With Writer's Block By (Answer If Applicable):

The Characters (If Applicable):

Today's Writing

My Beautiful Story

Date:

I Feel:

Today I Was Inspired By:

The Conveying Message:

Today's Writing Topic:

The What Ifs/How In What Your Writing
(Answer If Applicable):

Today's Emotions:

Today I Dealt With Writer's Block By
(Answer If Applicable):

The Characters (If Applicable):

Today's Writing

I Want To Outdo Myself In....

I REST AFTER I WRITE BECAUSE I JUST POURED ALL MY ENERGY INTO WHAT I NEEDED TO CONVEY.

My Beautiful Story

Date:

I Feel:

Today I Was Inspired By:

The Conveying Message:

Today's Writing Topic:

The What Ifs/How In What Your Writing (Answer If Applicable):

Today's Emotions:

Today I Dealt With Writer's Block By (Answer If Applicable):

The Characters (If Applicable):

Today's Writing

My Beautiful Story

Date:

I Feel:

Today I Was Inspired By:

The Conveying Message:

Today's Writing Topic:

The What Ifs/How In What Your Writing (Answer If Applicable):

Today's Emotions:

Today I Dealt With Writer's Block By (Answer If Applicable):

The Characters (If Applicable):

Today's Writing

My Beautiful Story

Date:

I Feel:

Today I Was Inspired By:

The Conveying Message:

Today's Writing Topic:

The What Ifs/How In What Your Writing (Answer If Applicable):

Today's Emotions:

Today I Dealt With Writer's Block By (Answer If Applicable):

The Characters (If Applicable):

Today's Writing

When I Start To Write, I Feel....

I TRAVEL BY WRITING.

My Beautiful Story

Date:

I Feel:

Today I Was Inspired By:

The Conveying Message:

Today's Writing Topic:

The What Ifs/How In What Your Writing (Answer If Applicable):

Today's Emotions:

Today I Dealt With Writer's Block By (Answer If Applicable):

The Characters (If Applicable):

Today's Writing

My Beautiful Story

Date:

I Feel:

Today I Was Inspired By:

The Conveying Message:

Today's Writing Topic:

The What Ifs/How In What Your Writing (Answer If Applicable):

Today's Emotions:

Today I Dealt With Writer's Block By (Answer If Applicable):

The Characters (If Applicable):

Today's Writing

My Beautiful Story

Date:

I Feel:

Today I Was Inspired By:

The Conveying Message:

Today's Writing Topic:

The What Ifs/How In What Your Writing (Answer If Applicable):

Today's Emotions:

Today I Dealt With Writer's Block By (Answer If Applicable):

The Characters (If Applicable):

Today's Writing

I WRITE BECAUSE I'VE EXPERIENCED SOME THINGS.

When I Don't Know How To Say What I Want To Say, I....

My Beautiful Story

Date:

I Feel:

Today I Was Inspired By:

The Conveying Message:

Today's Writing Topic:

The What Ifs/How In What Your Writing
(Answer If Applicable):

Today's Emotions:

Today I Dealt With Writer's Block By
(Answer If Applicable):

The Characters (If Applicable):

Today's Writing

My Beautiful Story

Date:

I Feel:

Today I Was Inspired By:

The Conveying Message:

Today's Writing Topic:

The What Ifs/How In What Your Writing (Answer If Applicable):

Today's Emotions:

Today I Dealt With Writer's Block By (Answer If Applicable):

The Characters (If Applicable):

Today's Writing

My Beautiful Story

Date:

I Feel:

Today I Was Inspired By:

The Conveying Message:

Today's Writing Topic:

The What Ifs/How In What Your Writing (Answer If Applicable):

Today's Emotions:

Today I Dealt With Writer's Block By (Answer If Applicable):

The Characters (If Applicable):

Today's Writing

When I Write, I Feel Like I'm Speaking To....

IF YOU WANT TO KNOW MORE ABOUT ME, READ WHAT I WRITE.

My Beautiful Story

Date:

I Feel:

Today I Was Inspired By:

The Conveying Message:

Today's Writing Topic:

The What Ifs/How In What Your Writing
(Answer If Applicable):

Today's Emotions:

Today I Dealt With Writer's Block By
(Answer If Applicable):

The Characters (If Applicable):

Today's Writing

My Beautiful Story

Date:

I Feel:

Today I Was Inspired By:

The Conveying Message:

Today's Writing Topic:

The What Ifs/How In What Your Writing (Answer If Applicable):

Today's Emotions:

Today I Dealt With Writer's Block By (Answer If Applicable):

The Characters (If Applicable):

Today's Writing

My Beautiful Story

Date:

I Feel:

Today I Was Inspired By:

The Conveying Message:

Today's Writing Topic:

The What Ifs/How In What Your Writing (Answer If Applicable):

Today's Emotions:

Today I Dealt With Writer's Block By (Answer If Applicable):

The Characters (If Applicable):

Today's Writing

My Beautiful Story

Date:

I Feel:

Today I Was Inspired By:

The Conveying Message:

Today's Writing Topic:

The What Ifs/How In What Your Writing
(Answer If Applicable):

Today's Emotions:

Today I Dealt With Writer's Block By
(Answer If Applicable):

The Characters (If Applicable):

Today's Writing

YOU DON'T WAIT TILL YOU FEEL LIKE WRITING TO WRITE.

Once I'm Done Writing, My Signature Piece Will Be....

My Beautiful Story

Date:

I Feel:

Today I Was Inspired By:

The Conveying Message:

Today's Writing Topic:

The What Ifs/How In What Your Writing (Answer If Applicable):

Today's Emotions:

Today I Dealt With Writer's Block By (Answer If Applicable):

The Characters (If Applicable):

Today's Writing

My Beautiful Story

Date:

I Feel:

Today I Was Inspired By:

The Conveying Message:

Today's Writing Topic:

The What Ifs/How In What Your Writing (Answer If Applicable):

Today's Emotions:

Today I Dealt With Writer's Block By (Answer If Applicable):

The Characters (If Applicable):

Today's Writing

My Beautiful Story

Date:

I Feel:

Today I Was Inspired By:

The Conveying Message:

Today's Writing Topic:

The What Ifs/How In What Your Writing (Answer If Applicable):

Today's Emotions:

Today I Dealt With Writer's Block By (Answer If Applicable):

The Characters (If Applicable):

Today's Writing

When I'm Done Writing And Go Back To Read My Work, I Usually Think....

SOMETIMES YOUR WORDS WILL BE THE ONLY THING THAT UNDERSTANDS YOU.

My Beautiful Story

Date:

I Feel:

Today I Was Inspired By:

The Conveying Message:

Today's Writing Topic:

The What Ifs/How In What Your Writing (Answer If Applicable):

Today's Emotions:

Today I Dealt With Writer's Block By (Answer If Applicable):

The Characters (If Applicable):

Today's Writing

My Beautiful Story

Date:

I Feel:

Today I Was Inspired By:

The Conveying Message:

Today's Writing Topic:

The What Ifs/How In What Your Writing
(Answer If Applicable):

Today's Emotions:

Today I Dealt With Writer's Block By
(Answer If Applicable):

The Characters (If Applicable):

Today's Writing

My Beautiful Story

Date: I Feel:

Today I Was Inspired By: The Conveying Message:

Today's Writing Topic: The What Ifs/How In What Your Writing
                                         (Answer If Applicable):

Today's Emotions: Today I Dealt With Writer's Block By
                                         (Answer If Applicable):

The Characters (If Applicable):

Today's Writing

My Beautiful Story

Date:

I Feel:

Today I Was Inspired By:

The Conveying Message:

Today's Writing Topic:

The What Ifs/How In What Your Writing (Answer If Applicable):

Today's Emotions:

Today I Dealt With Writer's Block By (Answer If Applicable):

The Characters (If Applicable):

Today's Writing

I CLOSED SOME DOORS WITH MY WRITING AND OPENED UP SOME NEW ONES.

I Want The Cover Of My Book!
Song To Look Like....

My Beautiful Story

Date:

I Feel:

Today I Was Inspired By:

The Conveying Message:

Today's Writing Topic:

The What Ifs/How In What Your Writing (Answer If Applicable):

Today's Emotions:

Today I Dealt With Writer's Block By (Answer If Applicable):

The Characters (If Applicable):

Today's Writing

My Beautiful Story

Date:

I Feel:

Today I Was Inspired By:

The Conveying Message:

Today's Writing Topic:

The What Ifs/How In What Your Writing (Answer If Applicable):

Today's Emotions:

Today I Dealt With Writer's Block By (Answer If Applicable):

The Characters (If Applicable):

Today's Writing

My Beautiful Story

Date:

I Feel:

Today I Was Inspired By:

The Conveying Message:

Today's Writing Topic:

The What Ifs/How In What Your Writing (Answer If Applicable):

Today's Emotions:

Today I Dealt With Writer's Block By (Answer If Applicable):

The Characters (If Applicable):

Today's Writing

My Beautiful Story

Date:

I Feel:

Today I Was Inspired By:

The Conveying Message:

Today's Writing Topic:

The What Ifs/How In What Your Writing (Answer If Applicable):

Today's Emotions:

Today I Dealt With Writer's Block By (Answer If Applicable):

The Characters (If Applicable):

Today's Writing

I'LL ALWAYS LIVE LONG BECAUSE MY WRITINGS WILL SPEAK FOR ME.

I HAVE A VOICE THAT WILL MAKE A DIFFERENCE.

My Beautiful Story

Date:

I Feel:

Today I Was Inspired By:

The Conveying Message:

Today's Writing Topic:

The What Ifs/How In What Your Writing (Answer If Applicable):

Today's Emotions:

Today I Dealt With Writer's Block By (Answer If Applicable):

The Characters (If Applicable):

Today's Writing

My Beautiful Story

Date:

I Feel:

Today I Was Inspired By:

The Conveying Message:

Today's Writing Topic:

The What Ifs/How In What Your Writing (Answer If Applicable):

Today's Emotions:

Today I Dealt With Writer's Block By (Answer If Applicable):

The Characters (If Applicable):

Today's Writing

My Beautiful Story

Date:

I Feel:

Today I Was Inspired By:

The Conveying Message:

Today's Writing Topic:

The What Ifs/How In What Your Writing
(Answer If Applicable):

Today's Emotions:

Today I Dealt With Writer's Block By
(Answer If Applicable):

The Characters (If Applicable):

Today's Writing

My Beautiful Story

Date:

I Feel:

Today I Was Inspired By:

The Conveying Message:

Today's Writing Topic:

The What Ifs/How In What Your Writing
(Answer If Applicable):

Today's Emotions:

Today I Dealt With Writer's Block By
(Answer If Applicable):

The Characters (If Applicable):

Today's Writing

THERE IS PEACE IN JUST BEING ME.

My Creative Thoughts Come To Me....

My Beautiful Story

Date:

I Feel:

Today I Was Inspired By:

The Conveying Message:

Today's Writing Topic:

The What Ifs/How In What Your Writing (Answer If Applicable):

Today's Emotions:

Today I Dealt With Writer's Block By (Answer If Applicable):

The Characters (If Applicable):

Today's Writing

My Beautiful Story

Date: I Feel:

Today I Was Inspired By: The Conveying Message:

Today's Writing Topic: The What Ifs/How In What Your Writing
                                               (Answer If Applicable):

Today's Emotions: Today I Dealt With Writer's Block By
                                               (Answer If Applicable):

The Characters (If Applicable):

Today's Writing

My Beautiful Story

Date:

I Feel:

Today I Was Inspired By:

The Conveying Message:

Today's Writing Topic:

The What Ifs/How In What Your Writing (Answer If Applicable):

Today's Emotions:

Today I Dealt With Writer's Block By (Answer If Applicable):

The Characters (If Applicable):

Today's Writing

My Beautiful Story

Date:

I Feel:

Today I Was Inspired By:

The Conveying Message:

Today's Writing Topic:

The What Ifs/How In What Your Writing (Answer If Applicable):

Today's Emotions:

Today I Dealt With Writer's Block By (Answer If Applicable):

The Characters (If Applicable):

Today's Writing

When I See Grammatical Mistakes, I....

I GROW BY CHALLENGING MYSELF IN MY WRITINGS.

My Beautiful Story

Date:

I Feel:

Today I Was Inspired By:

The Conveying Message:

Today's Writing Topic:

The What Ifs/How In What Your Writing (Answer If Applicable):

Today's Emotions:

Today I Dealt With Writer's Block By (Answer If Applicable):

The Characters (If Applicable):

Today's Writing

My Beautiful Story

Date:

I Feel:

Today I Was Inspired By:

The Conveying Message:

Today's Writing Topic:

The What Ifs/How In What Your Writing (Answer If Applicable):

Today's Emotions:

Today I Dealt With Writer's Block By (Answer If Applicable):

The Characters (If Applicable):

Today's Writing

My Beautiful Story

Date:

I Feel:

Today I Was Inspired By:

The Conveying Message:

Today's Writing Topic:

The What Ifs/How In What Your Writing (Answer If Applicable):

Today's Emotions:

Today I Dealt With Writer's Block By (Answer If Applicable):

The Characters (If Applicable):

Today's Writing

My Beautiful Story

Date:

I Feel:

Today I Was Inspired By:

The Conveying Message:

Today's Writing Topic:

The What Ifs/How In What Your Writing (Answer If Applicable):

Today's Emotions:

Today I Dealt With Writer's Block By (Answer If Applicable):

The Characters (If Applicable):

Today's Writing

My Beautiful Story

Date:

I Feel:

Today I Was Inspired By:

The Conveying Message:

Today's Writing Topic:

The What Ifs/How In What Your Writing (Answer If Applicable):

Today's Emotions:

Today I Dealt With Writer's Block By (Answer If Applicable):

The Characters (If Applicable):

Today's Writing

WHATEVER
YOU WILL
READ FROM ME
WILL INSPIRE
YOU.

YOU COULD WRITE A NOVEL BUT ARE YOU WILLING TO?

My Beautiful Story

Date:

I Feel:

Today I Was Inspired By:

The Conveying Message:

Today's Writing Topic:

The What Ifs/How In What Your Writing (Answer If Applicable):

Today's Emotions:

Today I Dealt With Writer's Block By (Answer If Applicable):

The Characters (If Applicable):

Today's Writing

My Beautiful Story

Date:

I Feel:

Today I Was Inspired By:

The Conveying Message:

Today's Writing Topic:

The What Ifs/How In What Your Writing (Answer If Applicable):

Today's Emotions:

Today I Dealt With Writer's Block By (Answer If Applicable):

The Characters (If Applicable):

Today's Writing

My Beautiful Story

Date:

I Feel:

Today I Was Inspired By:

The Conveying Message:

Today's Writing Topic:

The What Ifs/How In What Your Writing (Answer If Applicable):

Today's Emotions:

Today I Dealt With Writer's Block By (Answer If Applicable):

The Characters (If Applicable):

Today's Writing

My Beautiful Story

Date:

I Feel:

Today I Was Inspired By:

The Conveying Message:

Today's Writing Topic:

The What Ifs/How In What Your Writing (Answer If Applicable):

Today's Emotions:

Today I Dealt With Writer's Block By (Answer If Applicable):

The Characters (If Applicable):

Today's Writing

Old Writings I Have Found....

WRITING UNTIL MY DREAMS COME TRUE.

My Beautiful Story

Date:

I Feel:

Today I Was Inspired By:

The Conveying Message:

Today's Writing Topic:

The What Ifs/How In What Your Writing (Answer If Applicable):

Today's Emotions:

Today I Dealt With Writer's Block By (Answer If Applicable):

The Characters (If Applicable):

Today's Writing

My Beautiful Story

Date:

I Feel:

Today I Was Inspired By:

The Conveying Message:

Today's Writing Topic:

The What Ifs/How In What Your Writing (Answer If Applicable):

Today's Emotions:

Today I Dealt With Writer's Block By (Answer If Applicable):

The Characters (If Applicable):

Today's Writing

EVERYONE FALLS
IN LOVE WITH THE
WRITER AND THE
WRITER'S WORDS,
BUT NOT EVERYONE
WANTS TO WRITE.

Made in the USA
Columbia, SC
18 February 2021